STARS

AS

THE HOLIDAYMAKER

Charles M. Schulz

RAVETTE BOOKS

First published by
Ravette Books Limited 1990

Printed and bound in Great Britain
for Ravette Books Limited,
3 Glenside Estate, Star Road, Partridge Green,
Horsham, West Sussex RH13 8RA
by Cox & Wyman Ltd, Reading

ISBN 1 85304 235 8

PEANUTS
Tm Reg U S Pat Off All rights reserved © 1971 by United Feature Syndicate, Inc.
I GOT A VALENTINE FROM JOYCE!
2-15

AND I GOT ONE FROM SHIRLEY, AND FROM BARBARA, AND FROM SUE, AND FROM VIRGINIA, AND FROM PAT, AND FROM KAY, AND..

I HATE SOMEONE WHO GLOATS OVER ALL HIS VALENTINES!

THE FIFTEENTH OF FEBRUARY IS ALWAYS "GLOAT DAY"!
SCHULZ

PEANUTS
AND I GOT A VALENTINE FROM DONNA, AND FROM AMY, AND FROM JILL...

AND I GOT ONE FROM CHARLENE, AND FROM MARTHA, AND FROM...
IT'S VERY GAUCHE TO BRAG ABOUT ALL YOUR VALENTINES!
2-16

IT IS?

OH, WELL! AND I GOT ONE FROM JOAN, AND FROM QUINTANA, AND FROM MEREDITH, AND FROM...
SIGH

PEANUTS
Tm. Reg. U.S. Pat. Off.—All rights reserved
© 1969 by United Feature Syndicate, Inc.

TRICK OR TREAT

10-31
SMAK

THAT'S THE BEST TREAT YOU'LL GET ALL NIGHT, SWEETIE!

PEANUTS
11-1

HOW DO YOU TELL A PUMPKIN THAT YOU DON'T NEED HIM ANY MORE?
SCHULZ

PEANUTS
I SUPPOSE YOU'RE WONDERING WHAT I'M DOING...
11-24

I'M ADDRESSING TURKEY CARDS

© 1969 by United Feature Syndicate, Inc

AS LONG AS I'VE LIVED, I'VE NEVER RECEIVED A TURKEY CARD
SCHULZ

PEANUTS
HERE YOU ARE, SNOOPY...HAPPY THANKSGIVING!

THANK YOU

11-23
Tm Reg U.S. Pat Off --All rights reserved
© 1967 by United Feature Syndicate, Inc

NO CRANBERRIES?
SCHULZ

PEANUTS

10-26

NOT VERY FRIENDLY..
SCHULZ

PEANUTS
YOU KNOW WHAT TODAY IS?

11-3
TODAY IS ELECTION DAY

SMAK
I'D VOTE FOR YOU ANY DAY, SWEETIE..

..BUT I'M NOT REGISTERED!
SCHULZ

HERE WE ARE, SNOOPY, SITTING IN A PUMPKIN PATCH WAITING FOR THE "GREAT PUMPKIN"

EVERY HALLOWEEN THE GREAT PUMPKIN FLIES THROUGH THE AIR WITH HIS BAG OF TOYS

AND JUST THINK..IF YOU AND I SIT HERE ALL NIGHT, WE MAY GET TO SEE HIM!
Tm. Reg. U. S. Pat. Off.—All rights reserved
© 1971 by United Feature Syndicate, Inc.

I REALLY APPRECIATE YOUR SITTING OUT HERE WITH ME, SNOOPY...
10-31

I MUST ADMIT, HOWEVER, THAT I'VE BEEN WONDERING WHY YOU'RE WEARING THOSE DARK GLASSES...

THERE ARE CERTAIN TIMES WHEN YOU PREFER NOT TO BE RECOGNIZED!
SCHULZ

MMMMM

GET AWAY FROM HERE, YOU STUPID BEAGLE! I'M WAITING FOR SOMEONE MORE IMPORTANT..
BOOT!

BOOT!

AUGH!
12-27

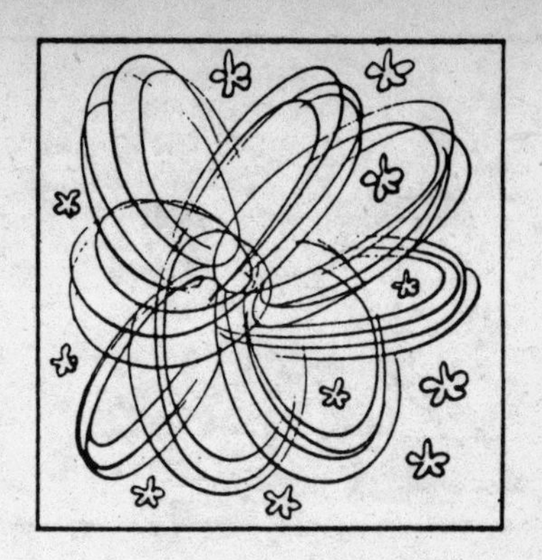

FIGHTING BENEATH THE MISTLETOE? HOW UNFEMININE..HOW UNROMANTIC... HOW GAUCHE!

WE WOULDN'T WANT TO BE GAUCHE, WOULD WE, SWEETIE? HAPPY HOLIDAYS!
SMAK!
SCHULZ

MUSTN'T
TOUCH!!

A PACKAGE JUST CAME FOR YOU, BUT IT SAYS, "DO NOT OPEN UNTIL CHRISTMAS"
12-23

DOGS CAN'T READ! HEE HEE HEE!!

HOW NICE! A NEW STOCKING CAP

HE WAS RIGHT.. I SHOULD HAVE WAITED...

NOW, EVERYONE ELSE WILL BE OPENING PRESENTS, BUT I'LL JUST HAVE TO STAND AROUND AND WATCH! RATS!

I'M SO STUPID!

I DO THIS EVERY YEAR

SURPRISE! ANOTHER PACKAGE JUST CAME, BUT IT SAYS, "DO NOT OPEN UNTIL.."
WHO CARES?

I CAN'T WAIT! I CAN'T WAIT!

I'M SO STUPID!
SCHULZ

REALLY?

A NEW YEAR'S PARTY? WITH LOTS OF GUESTS? AND WE'RE INVITED?

© 1984 United Feature Syndicate, Inc.
WAIT'LL I GET MY PARTY HAT...

I LOVE NEW YEAR'S PARTIES...

ESPECIALLY WHEN THERE'S A BIG CROWD AND LOTS OF CHICKS...

WOODSTOCK WAS RIGHT...FROM HERE IT DOES LOOK LIKE A BIG CROWD..

!
12-30

I'LL PROBABLY NEVER FORGIVE HIM FOR THIS!
SCHULZ

I JUST SHOOK HANDS WITH THE EASTER BEAGLE, AND HE GAVE ME A COLORED EGG!
4-11

SMAK!

THE "EASTER BEAGLE"?
Tm. Reg. U.S. Pat. Off.—All rights reserved
© 1971 by United Feature Syndicate, Inc.
SCHULZ

PEANUTS

THERE'S A GREAT BIG PURPLE AND GREEN AND YELLOW SPIDER WITH FORTY THOUSAND LEGS CRAWLING UP YOUR BACK!
4-1

NOBODY EVER BELIEVES MY APRIL FOOL JOKES
SCHULZ

NOW, THIS WILL BE SORT OF A REHEARSAL FOR TOMORROW NIGHT, SNOOPY...

TOMORROW IS HALLOWEEN, AND ON HALLOWEEN NIGHT THE GREAT PUMPKIN RISES OUT OF THE PUMPKIN PATCH, AND BRINGS TOYS TO ALL THE CHILDREN IN THE WORLD...

YOUR JOB IS TO BE KIND OF A PAUL REVERE...WHEN THE GREAT PUMPKIN COMES, YOU'LL GET ON YOUR HORSE, AND RIDE THROUGH THE COUNTRYSIDE SPREADING THE NEWS!
© 1977 United Feature Syndicate, Inc.

OKAY, LET'S REHEARSE IT..

HE'S COMING! HE'S COMING! THE GREAT PUMPKIN IS COMING!

RIDE, SNOOPY, RIDE! SPREAD THE NEWS!
I FEEL LIKE SUCH A FOOL!
SCHULZ
10-30

PEANUTS
Tm Reg U.S. Pat Off —All rights reserved © 1972 by United Feature Syndicate, Inc.
12-2

WOODSTOCK THINKS THAT IF YOU SIT IN A MAILBOX LONG ENOUGH, YOU'LL GET A CHRISTMAS CARD... HE'S SO NAIVE... HE JUST..

SCHULZ

I'LL READ THE LIST, AND YOU CAN TELL ME WHAT YOU WANT TO DO..

DO YOU WANT TO SEND A CHRISTMAS CARD TO MILLIE ?
12-17

NO, LET'S FORGET MILLIE... I DON'T THINK SHE REALLY LIKES ME..

HOW ABOUT THE O'HARAS ?
I DON'T KNOW... IT'S KIND OF HARD TO DECIDE...

THERE'S TINA... HOW ABOUT TINA?
TINA LIKES ME, BUT I DON'T KNOW...

HOW ABOUT JANET?
WELL, MAYBE...

I KNOW YOU DON'T WANT TO SEND A CARD TO 'POOCHIE'
I'M GLAD YOU KNOW THAT!

KIM? RANDI? NORMA?
NOPE! NOPE! NOPE!

HOW ABOUT AMY? I THINK AMY SHOULD GET A CARD
MAYBE YOU'RE RIGHT

THAT'S THE TROUBLE WITH HAVING ONLY ONE STAMP...
SCHULZ

OKAY, IT'S SETTLED..YOU'LL SEND A CARD TO AMY...I'LL MAIL IT OUT TODAY...
THANK YOU

PEANUTS
I CAN SEE MYSELF!

12-23

Tm. Reg. U S Pat. Off.—All rights reserved
© 1972 by United Feature Syndicate, Inc.

I'D LOOK FUNNY WITH A BIG NOSE..
SCHULZ

Dear Santa Claus,

OKAY, NOW YOU TELL ME WHAT YOU WANT HIM TO BRING YOU, AND I'LL PUT IT IN THE LETTER...

WHAT COLOR?
12-2
© 1982 United Feature Syndicate, Inc.
SCHULZ

PEANUTS
WOW!! I CAN'T BELIEVE IT!
1-1

WHAT A NIGHT...

THAT WOODSTOCK GIVES SOME WILD PARTIES!

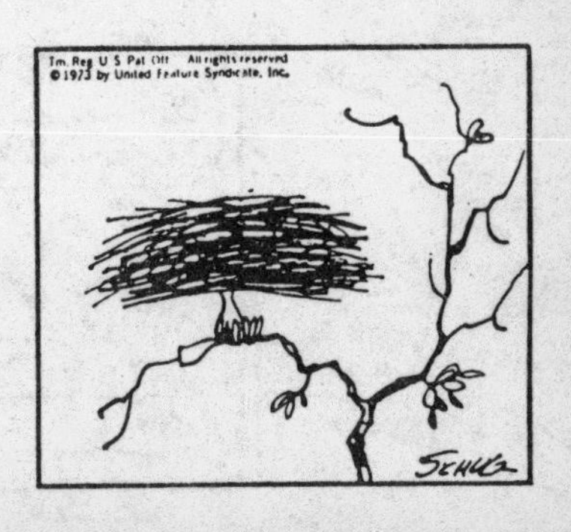
Tm. Reg U S Pat Off All rights reserved
© 1973 by United Feature Syndicate, Inc.

PEANUTS
HERE..IT LOOKS LIKE YOU GOT A BILL FROM WOODSTOCK
A BILL? FOR WHAT?
1-3

"YOU OWE ME SIX DOLLARS FOR THE THINGS YOU BROKE AT MY NEW YEAR'S PARTY... PLEASE PAY AT ONCE!"

THAT STUPID BIRD! HIS WHOLE NEST ISN'T WORTH SIX DOLLARS! I WON'T PAY!

BESIDES, HE SERVED VERY CHEAP ROOT BEER
SCHULZ

PEANUTS
WHAT'S THIS, ANOTHER BILL FROM WOODSTOCK?
1-4

"THIS IS YOUR SECOND NOTICE.. YOU OWE ME SIX DOLLARS FOR WHAT YOU BROKE AT MY NEW YEAR'S PARTY!"

"DON'T TRY TO GET OUT OF PAYING, BANANA NOSE!"
Tm. Reg. U.S. Pat. Off.—All rights reserved © 1973 by United Feature Syndicate, Inc.

BANANA NOSE?
SCHULZ

PEANUTS
1-5

POKE!
Tm Reg. U.S. Pat. Off.—All rights reserved
©1973 by United Feature Syndicate, Inc.

SCHULZ

PEANUTS
FRIENDSHIPS ARE TOO IMPORTANT TO SPOIL BY BICKERING..
TRUE
1-6

I THINK YOU AND WOODSTOCK SHOULD TRY TO TALK THINGS OUT...
HA! I CAN HEAR HIM NOW...

Tm. Reg. U.S. Pat. Off.—All rights reserved © 1973 by United Feature Syndicate, Inc.

I SEE WHAT YOU MEAN
THANK YOU
SCHULZ

PEANUTS
"THIS IS YOUR THIRD NOTICE! YOU OWE ME SIX DOLLARS FOR WHAT YOU BROKE AT MY NEW YEAR'S PARTY!"
1-8

SO PAY UP!!

MEOW!
Tm Reg U.S. Pat Off — All rights reserved
© 1973 by United Feature Syndicate, Inc

CATS HAVE THE RIGHT IDEA!
SCHULZ

PEANUTS
I HAVE A SUGGESTION
DOESN'T EVERYONE?

WHY DON'T YOU TRY TO FIND OUT WHAT IT WAS THAT YOU BROKE AT WOODSTOCK'S PARTY?
1-10

MAYBE THAT WOULD BE THE FIRST STEP TOWARD YOUR RECONCILIATION..

I ALWAYS TRIP ON THAT FIRST STEP
SCHULZ

PEANUTS
DO I HEAR THE FLUTTER OF WINGS?
1-11

RATS! IT'S ONLY A LEAF! I THOUGHT IT MIGHT BE WOODSTOCK..
Tm Reg U S Pat Off —All rights reserved
©1973 by United Feature Syndicate Inc

MAYBE I SHOULD WALK OVER TO SEE HIM...MAYBE WE CAN HAVE A LITTLE TALK, AND GET THINGS SETTLED....I'LL DO IT!!

SCHULZ

PEANUTS
WOODSTOCK! THAT WAS WOODSTOCK WHO JUST FLEW OVER!
1-12

HE WAS GOING TO SEE ME, AND I WAS GOING TO SEE HIM!

BONK!

EVEN ON A CLEAR DAY, WOODSTOCK FLIES IN A FOG!

PEANUTS
WE'LL GO OVER TO MY HOUSE...

WE'LL QUAFF A FEW ROOT BEERS, AND WE'LL SETTLE OUR DIFFERENCES LIKE CIVILIZED GENTLEMEN...

GULP GULP GULP
QUAFF QUAFF QUAFF
1-13

IT NEVER FAILS...THREE ROOT BEERS AND WOODSTOCK FALLS SOUND ASLEEP!
Z
SCHULZ

PEANUTS
"I INVITED YOU TO MY NEW YEAR'S PARTY BECAUSE YOU ARE MY FRIEND"

"THERE WAS SOMEONE ELSE AT THE PARTY THAT I WANTED YOU TO MEET"
1-15

"SHE'S THE CUTEST LITTLE BIRD I'VE EVER KNOWN, AND YOU MONOPOLIZED HER THE WHOLE EVENING.."

"IT BROKE MY HEART.....THAT'S WHY I SENT YOU A BILL FOR SIX DOLLARS.."
SCHULZ

PEANUTS
I SPOILED WOODSTOCK'S PARTY!
1-16

HE HAD INVITED THIS CUTE LITTLE BIRD THAT HE'S IN LOVE WITH, BUT HE NEVER GOT TO TALK WITH HER BECAUSE I TALKED WITH HER THE WHOLE EVENING!

SO HE SENT ME A BILL FOR SIX DOLLARS FOR A BROKEN HEART! OH, WOODSTOCK, MY LITTLE FRIEND OF FRIENDS...

DON'T YOU REALIZE THAT YOUR HEART IS WORTH MUCH MUCH MORE THAN SIX DOLLARS?!!
SIGH
SCHULZ

HE'S COMING! HE'S COMING!

THANK YOU, EASTER BEAGLE! THANK YOU!

THANK YOU

THANK YOU VERY MUCH

THANK YOU
4-22

THANK YOU!

EVERYBODY GETS AN EGG FROM THE EASTER BEAGLE

WHO DO I GET ONE FROM?

HIS ASSISTANT!
SCHULZ
Tm Reg U.S. Pat Off —All rights reserved
©1973 by United Feature Syndicate Inc

PEANUTS
WHAT A BEAUTIFUL NIGHT..

THE MOON IS FULL..

..AND THERE MUST BE A BILLION STARS IN THE SKY..
7-30

IT'S A PERFECT NIGHT TO GET A STAR-TAN..
SCHULZ

NEXT SUNDAY IS MOTHER'S DAY...
IT IS ?
5-7

YOU SHOULD GIVE YOUR MOTHER A CALL..
© 1978 United Feature Syndicate, Inc.

OR AT LEAST WRITE HER A LETTER
HMM..

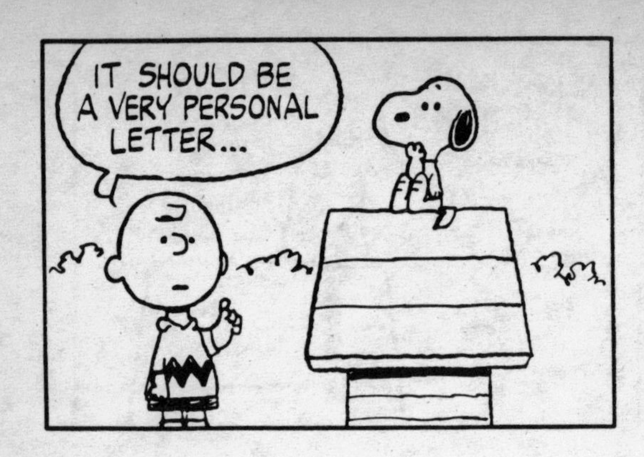
IT SHOULD BE A VERY PERSONAL LETTER...

THE KIND THAT COULD COME ONLY FROM YOU...

Dear Mom,
SCHULZ

IF YOU LOOK AT THE CALENDAR TOO MUCH, IT'LL DRIVE YOU CRAZY

TODAY IS FATHER'S DAY... I LOVED MY DAD..I THINK ABOUT HIM A LOT...

HE WAS THE ONE WHO TAUGHT US THE OL' CHESHIRE CAT TRICK...

YOU JUST GRADUALLY FADE AWAY UNTIL ONLY YOUR GRIN IS LEFT

ONE DAY DAD ACTUALLY DID DISAPPEAR..WE NEVER KNEW WHERE HE WENT..THAT'S THE TROUBLE WITH BEING A DOG...THEY NEVER TELL YOU ANYTHING...
© 1982 United Feature Syndicate, Inc.
6-20

NOW OUR FAMILY IS SCATTERED ALL OVER..SPIKE'S IN NEEDLES... BELLE'S IN KANSAS CITY..

I DON'T KNOW WHERE ANY OF THE OTHERS ARE...

ANYWAY, DAD, HAPPY FATHER'S DAY WHEREVER YOU ARE!

RATS!
SCHULZ

PEANUTS
I WONDER WHAT WOULD HAPPEN IF I TRIED TO MAKE FRIENDS WITH THAT STUPID CAT NEXT DOOR...

I COULD SHOW HIM MY GOOD WILL BY EXTENDING MY PAW IN FRIENDSHIP...
12-17

BY GOLLY, I'LL DO IT!

SCHULZ

PEANUTS
I HEAR YOU TRIED TO MAKE FRIENDS WITH THE CAT NEXT DOOR...
STUPID CAT!
12-19

I OFFERED HIM THE RIGHT HAND OF FELLOWSHIP, AND HE ALMOST TORE IT OFF!

MAYBE YOU SHOULDN'T HAVE BEEN WEARING A HOCKEY GLOVE... MAYBE HE THINKS YOU DON'T TRUST HIM...

I TRUST HIM, BUT MY HAND DOESN'T!
SCHULZ

PEANUTS
I THINK YOU SHOWED THE TRUE SPIRIT OF CHRISTMAS
I AGREE

BUT NOW I THINK YOU SHOULD TRY IT AGAIN...I THINK YOU SHOULD OFFER THE CAT NEXT DOOR YOUR RIGHT HAND OF FELLOWSHIP, BUT WITHOUT THE HOCKEY GLOVE...

WHAT ARE YOU DOING?
12-20

I'M HAVING A FAREWELL DINNER FOR MY HAND!
SCHULZ

PEANUTS
OKAY, CAT, THIS IS THE SEASON OF LOVE AND PEACE...
12-21

EVEN THOUGH I KNOW YOU HATE ME, I AM GOING TO EXTEND THE RIGHT HAND OF FELLOWSHIP...

SCHULZ

CHRISTMAS IS COMING, CHARLIE BROWN

I'VE MADE OUT A LIST TO HELP YOU DECIDE WHAT TO GET ME
12-4

WELL, MY HANDS ARE FULL RIGHT NOW..COULD YOU PUT IT SOME PLACE WHERE I'LL REMEMBER IT?

LUCY GAVE ME HER CHRISTMAS LIST, BUT I CAN'T REMEMBER WHERE I PUT IT...
12-5

I'VE GOT TO FIND THAT LIST...

I CAN'T IMAGINE WHERE IT COULD BE..

IF I DIDN'T HAVE TENURE, I THINK MAYBE I'D MOVE
SCHULZ
© 1979 United Feature Syndicate, Inc.

I'VE MADE UP A NEW LIST OF THINGS I WANT FOR CHRISTMAS, CHARLIE BROWN

I HATE TO ADMIT IT, BUT I CAN'T EVEN REMEMBER WHERE WE PUT THE OTHER LIST
12-6

DON'T WORRY, I KNOW JUST WHERE IT IS...
© 1979 United Feature Syndicate, Inc.

JOE SPINDLE!

YES, MA'AM, I'M LOOKING FOR A GIFT
© 1979 United Feature Syndicate, Inc.
12-7

IT'S FOR A FRIEND OF MINE..A GIRL...SHE GAVE ME A COUPLE OF LISTS OF THINGS SHE WANTS SO...

THE LISTS WERE RIGHT HERE..WHERE DID THEY GO?

I CAN HEAR THE TOY TRAINS, BUT I CAN'T SEE THEM..
SCHULZ

PEANUTS
YOU KNOW, I MAY HAVE BEEN WRONG ABOUT THOSE CHRISTMAS STOCKINGS...

IF YOU WANT TO HANG UP A CHRISTMAS STOCKING, LITTLE FRIEND, I THINK YOU SHOULD!

HANG UP AS MANY AS YOU WANT! MERRY CHRISTMAS!!
12-24

SCHULZ

PEANUTS
HERE COMES WOODSTOCK...
12-25

HE DOESN'T KNOW I GOT HIM SOMETHING FOR CHRISTMAS

I'M GONNA SURPRISE HIM, AND HANG THIS LITTLE CANDY CANE RIGHT ON HIS NOSE...

SCHULZ

YOUR SHAKE

WHAT'S THE MATTER?

LISTEN!
WHAT IS IT?

I THOUGHT I HEARD SOMETHING ON THE ROOF...
© 1978 United Feature Syndicate, Inc.
12-24

SANTA CLAUS?
REINDEER?

CAN YOU SEE ANYTHING, BIG BROTHER?
NO, IT'S TOO DARK... BESIDES, IT'S STARTING TO SNOW AGAIN...

DO YOU REALLY THINK IT COULD BE SANTA CLAUS AND HIS REINDEER?
WHY NOT? WHO ELSE COULD IT BE?

I HATE TO ADMIT IT, MEN, BUT I THINK WE'RE LOST AGAIN!
SCHULZ

PEANUTS
THE ORANGE WAS A GOOD IDEA, WASN'T IT?
12-23

I FIGURE IF YOU PUT THE ORANGE IN WOODSTOCK'S CHRISTMAS STOCKING, IT WILL MAKE HIM VERY HAPPY

I'M GLAD YOU AGREE THAT THE ORANGE IS A GOOD IDEA

THE ORANGE WAS A GREAT IDEA...EXCEPT I ATE IT!
SCHULZ

PEANUTS
POOR WOODSTOCK
12-25

HE'LL NEVER KNOW THE JOY OF WAKING UP ON CHRISTMAS MORNING, AND FINDING A NEW BICYCLE PARKED UNDER THE CHRISTMAS TREE...

I'D BETTER GO OVER, AND CONSOLE HIM...

SCHULZ

PEANUTS
HERE COMES WOODSTOCK ON HIS NEW BICYCLE...

12-26

I HATE IT WHEN HE SAYS, "LOOK, NO WINGS!"
SCHULZ

PEANUTS
Gentlemen,
I ordered a toy bicycle for my sister's doll set.

It was supposed to be here by Christmas. Perhaps it was delivered to the wrong address.

Would you look into the matter, please?
Thank you.

I REFUSE TO BE THE ONE WHO TELLS HIM!
SCHULZ
12-27

PEANUTS
I ORDERED A TOY BICYCLE FOR YOUR DOLL SET, BUT IT NEVER CAME...

I HAVE A FEELING IT WAS PROBABLY DELIVERED TO THE WRONG ADDRESS...

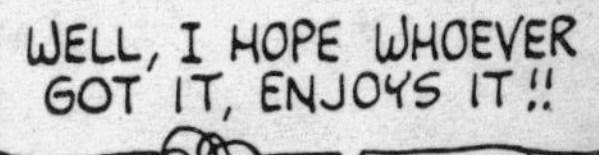
WELL, I HOPE WHOEVER GOT IT, ENJOYS IT!!

12-28

WHEELIES, YET! GOOD GRIEF!
SCHULZ

'79

AH!
WHAT A GREAT HAT!
12-31

I LOVE NEW YEAR'S PARTIES

I WONDER WHAT CONRAD, BILL, OLIVIER AND WOODSTOCK WILL WEAR...

THOSE BIRDS ARE WEIRD

I HOPE THEY REALIZE THAT WHEN YOU GO TO A NEW YEAR'S PARTY, YOU HAVE TO WEAR A GREAT HAT...

SCHULZ

PEANUTS
YOU'RE JUST NOW GETTING HOME FROM WOODSTOCK'S PARTY?
1-1

HOW DID YOU GET ALL WET?
Tm. Reg. U.S. Pat. Off.—All rights reserved © 1976 by United Feature Syndicate, Inc.

WELL, YOU KNOW HOW IT GOES...

FIRST ONE PERSON GETS PUSHED INTO THE BIRDBATH.. THEN ANOTHER...
SCHULZ

PEANUTS

2-12

WAITING FOR VALENTINES!
SCHULZ

PEANUTS

SIGH
SCHULZ

IS IT?
IT IS!

WOW!

HE'S COMING! HE'S COMING!
WHO? THE EASTER BEAGLE?

NO, NOT THE EASTER BEAGLE!
WHO? THE GREAT PUMPKIN?

NO, NO, NO!! NOT THE GREAT PUMPKIN!
© 1979 United Feature Syndicate, Inc.

WELL, THEN, WHO?

WHO'S COMING? WHO'S COMING?
4-1

THE APRIL FOOL!!
WHY CAN'T I HAVE A NORMAL DOG LIKE EVERYONE ELSE?
SCHULZ

4-14

THE EASTER BUNNY IS OUT IN OUR FRONT YARD!
SURE, HE IS..

HE'S HIDING EGGS...HE'S DOING A SPRING DANCE, AND HE'S HIDING EGGS ALL OVER THE FRONT LAWN...
UH HUH... SURE, HE IS...

I THINK I'LL GO OUT AND GATHER UP ALL THE EGGS
WHY DON'T YOU JUST DO THAT...

Tm. Reg. U. S. Pat. Off.—All rights reserved
© 1968 by United Feature Syndicate, Inc.

YOU MISS A LOT WHEN YOU SIT AND WATCH TV ALL DAY LONG...
SCHULZ

PEANUTS
YOU KNOW WHAT NEXT WEEK IS?

NEXT WEEK IS "NATIONAL CAT WEEK"

11-2
REALLY?

FORGET IT!
SCHULZ

PEANUTS
I KNOW THAT THE ONLY REASON I'M SITTING OUT HERE IS BECAUSE I'M SUPERSTITIOUS..

WHY ELSE WOULD I SIT IN A PUMPKIN PATCH ALL NIGHT WAITING FOR THE "GREAT PUMPKIN"?

OF COURSE, I'M THE TRUSTING TYPE, TOO... I'M TRUSTING AND FAITHFUL AND SUPERSTITIOUS...

LET'S FACE IT... I'M ALSO A LITTLE BIT STUPID!

A Thanksgiving Story
"You turkey!" she cried.
"Who's a turkey?"
"You, you turkey!"
© 1988 United Feature Syndicate, Inc.

"Listen to who's talking, you meat loaf!"
"I'd rather be a meat loaf than a turkey, you turkey!"

THANKSGIVING STORIES ARE HARD TO WRITE..
11-23

I'M GOING TO TRY TO SELL CHRISTMAS WREATHS FROM DOOR TO DOOR
12-14

GETTING ON THE OL' COMMERCIAL BANDWAGON, EH? GOING AFTER THOSE BIG HOLIDAY BUCKS, HUH?

NEED ANY HELP?
© 1982 United Feature Syndicate, Inc.
SCHULZ

GOOD MORNING...ASK YOUR MOM IF SHE'D LIKE TO BUY A CHRISTMAS WREATH

TELL HER THEY WERE MADE FROM THE FAMOUS FORESTS OF LEBANON
12-15

YOU CAN READ ABOUT 'EM IN THE SECOND CHAPTER OF THE SECOND BOOK OF CHRONICLES...
© 1982 United Feature Syndicate, Inc.

IF YOU BUY TWO, WE'LL THROW IN AN AUTOGRAPHED PHOTO OF KING SOLOMON!
SCHULZ

YOU CAN'T TELL PEOPLE THESE WREATHS WERE MADE FROM THE FORESTS OF LEBANON! THAT'S LYING!

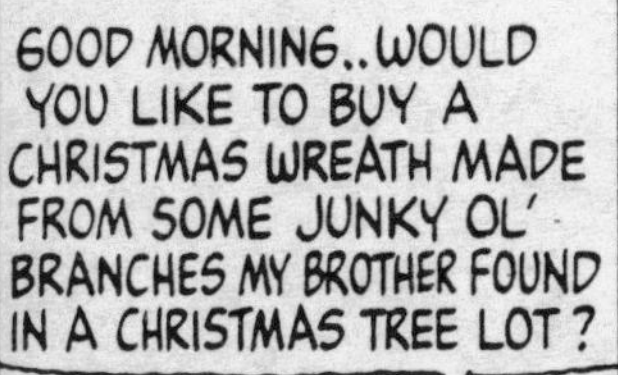
GOOD MORNING..WOULD YOU LIKE TO BUY A CHRISTMAS WREATH MADE FROM SOME JUNKY OL' BRANCHES MY BROTHER FOUND IN A CHRISTMAS TREE LOT?

YOU WOULDN'T, WOULD YOU? AND I CAN'T SAY I BLAME YOU!
12/16
© 1982 United Feature Syndicate, Inc.

SEE? YOUR WAY DOESN'T WORK, EITHER!

NO ONE SEEMS TO WANT TO BUY A CHRISTMAS WREATH

I THINK WE NEED BETTER PACKAGING

WE NEED A BETTER WAY TO SHOW OFF OUR PRODUCT...
12-17
© 1982 United Feature Syndicate, Inc.

GOOD MORNING! WOULD YOU LIKE TO BUY A CHRISTMAS WREATH?

GOOD MORNING, MA'AM

HOW WOULD YOU LIKE TO BUY A NICE CHRISTMAS NOSE?

I MEAN "WREATH"! HOW EMBARRASSING!!

I'M GOING HOME!
SCHULZ
© 1982 United Feature Syndicate, Inc.
12-18

GOOD MORNING, SIR... WOULD YOU LIKE TO BUY A NICE CHRISTMAS WREATH?

SLAM!

MERRY CHRISTMAS, ANYWAY, SIR! "'GOD BLESS US EVERY ONE!' SAID TINY TIM, THE LAST OF ALL."... AND JOY TO THE WORLD!

RATS!
SCHULZ
12-20
© 1982 United Feature Syndicate, Inc.

HEY, WAKE UP! LET'S GO SELL THOSE CHRISTMAS WREATHS!

WHETHER YOU LIKE IT OR NOT, YOU'RE MY SALES GIMMICK...
12-21

YAWN!

SCHULZ

YOU SOLD THREE CHRISTMAS WREATHS? WOW!!
I TOLD YOU I COULD!
© 1982 United Feature Syndicate, Inc.

THIS IS WHAT GETS THEIR ATTENTION..WHEN THEY SEE THE WREATH ON YOUR DOG'S NOSE, THEY CAN'T RESIST BUYING!

I'M NOT SATISFIED, HOWEVER..I THINK WE CAN DO EVEN BETTER...
12-22

MORE IS NOT NECESSARILY BETTER..
GOOD MORNING!

THIS IS A GREAT BUSINESS WE HAVE GOING HERE, BIG BROTHER...

YOU MAKE THE WREATHS, AND YOUR DOG AND I GO OUT AND SELL 'EM!

WE'LL SELL CHRISTMAS WREATHS TO EVERY HOME IN THE NEIGHBORHOOD
12-23

UNLESS MY NOSE FALLS OFF!
© 1982 United Feature Syndicate, Inc.

MAKE SOME MORE CHRISTMAS WREATHS, BIG BROTHER! I HAVE ORDERS FOR TEN MORE!
12-24

I CAN'T DO IT! LOOK AT MY FINGERS...

WELL, THERE GOES MY CHRISTMAS MONEY!
WHAT ABOUT MY FINGERS?

SCHULZ
THE OL' NOSE HAS A FEW QUESTIONS, TOO!
© 1982 United Feature Syndicate, Inc.

HE HAS THESE REINDEER, SEE, AND THEY FLY THROUGH THE AIR PULLING HIS SLED...
12-24

AND IF YOU BELIEVE THAT, I HAVE A GOLD BIRD NEST THAT I'LL SELL YOU FOR A DOLLAR!

HAHAHAHAHA!

MERRY CHRISTMAS, LITTLE FRIEND..
SCHULZ

I NEVER GET INVITED TO NEW YEAR'S PARTIES

TOMORROW NIGHT MILLIONS OF PEOPLE WILL BE DRESSING TO GO OUT...
© 1983 United Feature Syndicate, Inc.

SOME ARE EVEN READY A DAY AHEAD OF TIME...
12-30
SCHULZ

STUPID DOG!

NEW YEAR'S WAS FIVE DAYS AGO, AND THAT DOG IS STILL CELEBRATING!

TALK ABOUT BEING LATE...LET ME SHOW YOU SOMETHING...

MY DUMB BROTHER HERE IS JUST GETTING AROUND TO ADDRESSING HIS CHRISTMAS CARDS!

NOBODY COULD BE LATER THAN THAT!
1-5

Tm Reg U S Pat Off — All rights reserved
© 1975 by United Feature Syndicate, Inc
KNOCK
KNOCK
KNOCK

TRICK OR TREAT?!
SCHULZ

THAT'S RIGHT, CHUCK.. I'D ASK YOU, BUT I KNOW YOU CAN'T DANCE... AND BY THE WAY, DON'T SEND YOUR CRAZY DOG!

WHAT DO YOU THINK?

THIS IS A VALENTINE I BOUGHT FOR THAT LITTLE RED-HAIRED GIRL...

I WANT TO GO OVER TO HER HOUSE, AND GIVE IT TO HER, BUT I THINK I'D BE TOO NERVOUS TO DO IT WITHOUT PRACTICE...

I'LL GO OUTSIDE AND RING THE DOORBELL, AND YOU PRETEND YOU'RE THE LITTLE RED-HAIRED GIRL, OKAY?

2-10

© 1985 United Feature Syndicate, Inc.
RING!
SCHULZ

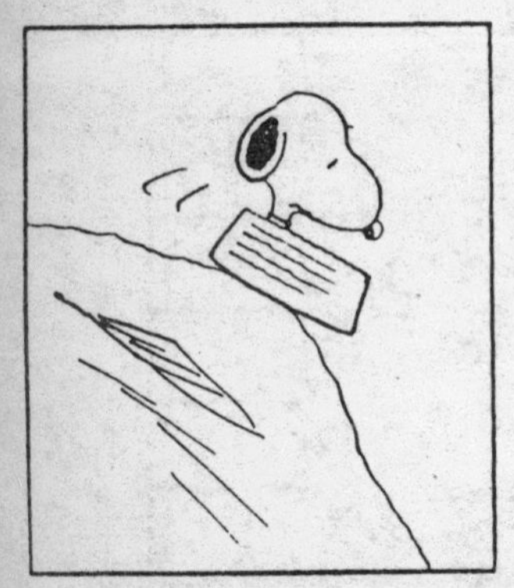

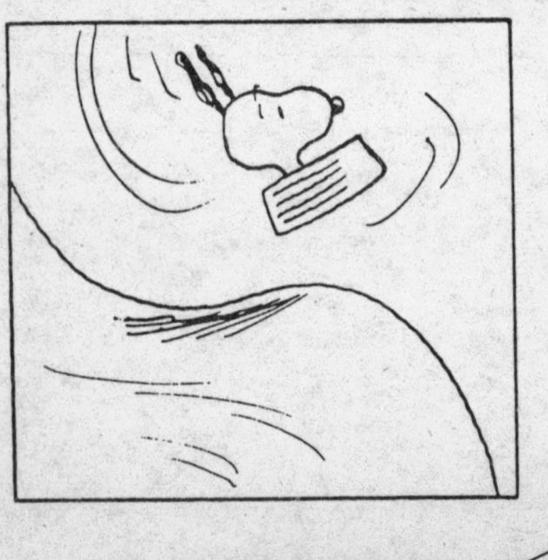

THUNK!

USUALLY, WHEN THEY COLLECT MONEY, THEY RING LITTLE BELLS..
SCHULZ

type
TYPE
type
type
TYPE

I'LL BET YOU FORGOT, DIDN'T YOU ?

TODAY IS MOTHER'S DAY!

5-11
IT'S A PERFECT TIME TO WRITE TO YOUR MOTHER..
© 1986 United Feature Syndicate, Inc.

LET HER KNOW YOU HAVEN'T FORGOTTEN HER

Dear Mom,
I remember
when I was
born.

It was a
dark and
stormy
night.
SCHULZ

PEANUTS
I HEAR YOU'RE GOING TO GIVE A FOURTH OF JULY SPEECH
6-30

I'D SUGGEST THAT YOU SPEAK ON THE NEW WOMEN'S LIBERATION MOVEMENT BECAUSE IT'S REALLY THE MOST IMPORTANT THING THAT..

SMAK

I DON'T RECALL ASKING FOR ANY ADVICE, SWEETIE!
SCHULZ

FOR YOUR DAD, HUH?

THAT'S RIGHT.. FOR FATHER'S DAY..

I JUST FOUND OUT THAT HE'S RETIRED NOW, AND LIVING IN FLORIDA...

THERE WERE EIGHT OF US IN THE LITTER

I KNOW HE'LL APPRECIATE GETTING THIS CARD...
U.S. MAIL

Dear Dad, Happy Father's Day!
AND THEY ALL SIGNED IT!
SCHULZ
6-18

4-23
© 1986 United Feature Syndicate, Inc.

AND A "HAPPY SECRETARIES DAY" TO YOU, TOO!
SCHULZ

IT SEEMS TO BE ALMOST A MYSTERY...
© 1981 United Feature Syndicate, Inc.

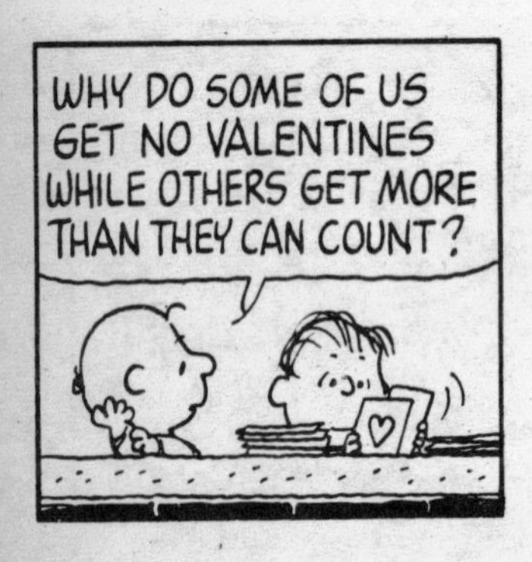
WHY DO SOME OF US GET NO VALENTINES WHILE OTHERS GET MORE THAN THEY CAN COUNT?

YOU'RE RIGHT, CHARLIE BROWN...IT SEEMS TO BE A MYSTERY...

AND THOSE OF US WHO KNOW, WON'T TELL!
2-14
SCHULZ

OKAY..
(c) 1988 United Feature Syndicate, Inc

10-10

I HATE DRINKING OUT OF A HOSE..
SCHULZ

HEY, DOG!

I'M GOING TO MAKE MY OWN VALENTINES THIS YEAR..

I'M GOING TO CUT OUT SOME PRETTY RED HEARTS, AND GLUE LACE AROUND THEM...

WHAT I WANT YOU TO DO IS TYPE OUT A NICE VERSE
© 1986 United Feature Syndicate, Inc.

Chocolate chip cookies are red.
Chocolate chip cookies are blue.
Chocolate chip cookies are sweet.
So are you.

THIS IS TERRIBLE! I CAN'T MAKE A VALENTINE WITH THAT! WRITE ANOTHER ONE!!
2-9

Angel food cake with seven-minute frosting is red...Angel food cake with seven-minute frosting is blue... Angel food cake with seven-minute frosting is sweet...So are you.

THAT'S THE DUMBEST THING I'VE EVER READ!

I GUESS I MISUNDERSTOOD... I THOUGHT SHE WANTED SOMETHING SENTIMENTAL..

HEY! WHERE'S EVERYBODY GOING? COME BACK!

IT'S GOING TO CLEAR UP!
© 1987 United Feature Syndicate, Inc.

THE SUN IS BREAKING THROUGH!
8-25

SORRY, I THOUGHT IT WAS THE SUN..

HEY, STUPID CAT! YOU MISSED MY BIRTHDAY AGAIN!
© 1977 United Feature Syndicate, Inc.

I KNOW HOW MUCH YOU LIKE ME...I THOUGHT MAYBE YOU'D GIVE ME A CAKE WITH SOME CANDLES ON IT...
10-24

SLASH

HOW NICE!
SCHULZ